"This book is dedicated to the approximately twelve thousand children each year who will discover that their brother or sister has cancer, and to my beloved son Oliver who kept me smiling."

Michael Dodd

For Moms and Dads

There is perhaps nothing more painful for a parent, than having to confront the serious illness of a child. The parent will find himself or herself pulled in so many directions at the same time—trying to comfort the child, trying to deal with one's own pain and fear, trying to ease the anguish of one's mate, and struggling to keep up with the demands of one's job with all that is going on. Almost inevitably, the other children in the family will sink to the bottom of the priority list. Surveys have found that when one child in a family was seriously ill, the parents insisted that "we made a point of not neglecting our other children," while the other children told interviewers "my parents were so distracted they didn't know I existed."

And yet brothers and sisters of an ailing child inevitably respond to the tension in the household. They may respond with genuine love and concern for the afflicted child. They may respond with fear that something similar might happen to them next, especially if they believe that sickness or accident was punishment for misbehavior. They may resent the attention lavished on the sibling and hate themselves for envying a suffering child. They may even feel guilty for being the healthy one.

That is why this book is such a welcome one. It does several important things and does them well. It gives voice to the love, the fear, and the confusion of the older brother. It gives concrete examples of things he can do to help his sister and overcome his feelings of helplessness as he does. And it describes ways in which he can go on with his own life and find it pleasant, tacitly giving him permission to do so, even when his sister is seriously ill and his parents are distracted.

It is a book to read and re-read with brothers and sisters of an ailing child. They will identify with its pictures, be comforted by its words, and be guided by its suggestions.

Rabbi Harold S. Kushner

For 'Sibs' of Kids with Cancer

This book tells a story about one child. But there is an important story to be told for every brother or sister of a child with cancer. That's because when you find out your brother or sister has cancer, all of a sudden, life can kind of get turned upside down.

You might feel scared that your brother or sister with cancer could die. Or, you might get scared that you will get cancer too, or that something bad could happen to someone else you know. You might get really mad that your sick brother or sister is getting all kinds of special attention and you're not. You might wonder if something you thought or did could have caused a brother or sister to get cancer, even though this is _never_ true. You might miss playing with your sick brother or sister, or just wish that things could be the way they were before cancer came along. You might be angry that your Mom or Dad is away at the hospital a lot, or that they don't spend as much time with you as they used to. All of these feelings are O.K. Remember, your feelings aren't the problem. Cancer is. And with difficult feelings, it usually helps to talk to someone you know and trust.

Whatever happens, don't forget that you are a very important person in your family. You are loved by your sick brother or sister, your Mom and your Dad, your friends, and everybody else. And just like before the cancer, they may ask for your help. Because you are a kid, you will find ways to help that your parents and doctors would never imagine. And you will make a big difference.

Michael Dodd

I remember when my sister had cancer. It was last summer.

I remember when my Mom and Dad first told me. They were very sad. I didn't have to ask why they were so sad. I felt sad too.

My Dad told me that sometimes kids with cancer don't get better. He was crying. My Dad doesn't usually cry, but I know that grown-ups can be afraid sometimes too. He said Isabelle would have to go to the hospital a lot for a whole year, but that he thought she would get better. I thought Isabelle would get better too. She's my little sister.

We went to Grammy and Grampy's house to see my cousins and friends. Grammy called this Isabelle's "Celebration of Life." My Mom and Dad said that my smile made them feel better, and would make Isabelle feel better too.

My Mom gave me five whole dollars to buy candy for me and all the kids. First, I tasted the candy. Then I said a prayer for Isabelle.

The next day, Isabelle went to the hospital for a biopsy. That's an operation where the doctor takes out a tiny piece of the cancer to do special tests. I made a pretend bird house and paper flowers to decorate Isabelle's hospital room. Real flowers aren't allowed, because they can give germs to kids in the hospital.

My Mom and Dad stayed with Isabelle
in the hospital overnight. I asked if I
could stay too, but hospital rules said no.
That made me really mad. I wanted
to be with my Mom and Dad,
and Isabelle all
the time.

Grammy and Grampy came to stay with me at my house. Grampy slept in my room the most.

Grammy said that's because me and Grampy snore a lot. I didn't feel so lonely when Grampy was in my bedroom.

I did a lot of fun things when Grammy and Grampy came to stay. Grampy took me fishing, and he took me and my best friend Mark to play miniature golf.

Grammy showed me
how to cook artichokes.
Sometimes she talked on
the phone about Isabelle's
cancer. I listened. Then I
asked questions about
what she was saying …
and what did
it mean.

At the hospital, Isabelle smiled
right away when she saw me. My Mom said that was the first time
Isabelle smiled since her operation. I can always make Isabelle smile.

At first, Isabelle was really scared of the nurses. But the nurses were always nice to me. Once I got to stay with Isabelle for her blood test. Isabelle screamed a lot, but I told her, " You'll be all right little one," and soon she was.

Sometimes people ask how I know so much about cancer. That's because of books. My favorite was "Kemo-Shark." It's about a pretend shark named "Kemo" who goes inside a person's body to kill the cancer—just like chemotherapy.

The only bad thing about "Kemo" is that he can make people feel tired, and throw up, and make their hair fall out.

When Isabelle's hair fell out, I knew that "Kemo-Shark" was really working to kill the cancer. I told everyone that Isabelle was the cutest bald baby on 7-West.

Sometimes, my best friend Mark came to visit me at the hospital. We visited Isabelle, and then we went exploring in the hospital and pretended to be spies.

I wanted to ride in the bike-a-thon to raise money
for cancer, but my Dad told me that kids weren't allowed.
So we collected money from the neighbors, and I bought Beanie
Babies to give to the kids every time I visited Isabelle at the hospital.

On the first day of school, I brought in a picture showing what I did over the summer. My teacher sent home a note saying I had a really good first day.

I saw two kids from school at the hospital a lot.
Julie's sister had an organ transplant, and Chrissy gets
physical therapy. On Fridays, me and Julie ate lunch with a
counselor named Mrs. Burlingham. Julie talks mostly, and I listen.

On Halloween, Isabelle couldn't go trick or treating because of germs. I collected candy for her, but after a while I just wanted to go home. I gave Isabelle my "SMARTIES" and she ate them really fast.

Before Thanksgiving Isabelle had her "big surgery" to take the cancer out. It lasted from morning until night. I stayed the whole time. Lots of people came to visit. It was my job to show them the hospital.

I had to wait two whole days to see Isabelle after her surgery. She was in the ICU. I said "Hi little one…" and she smiled at me, but only with her eyes.

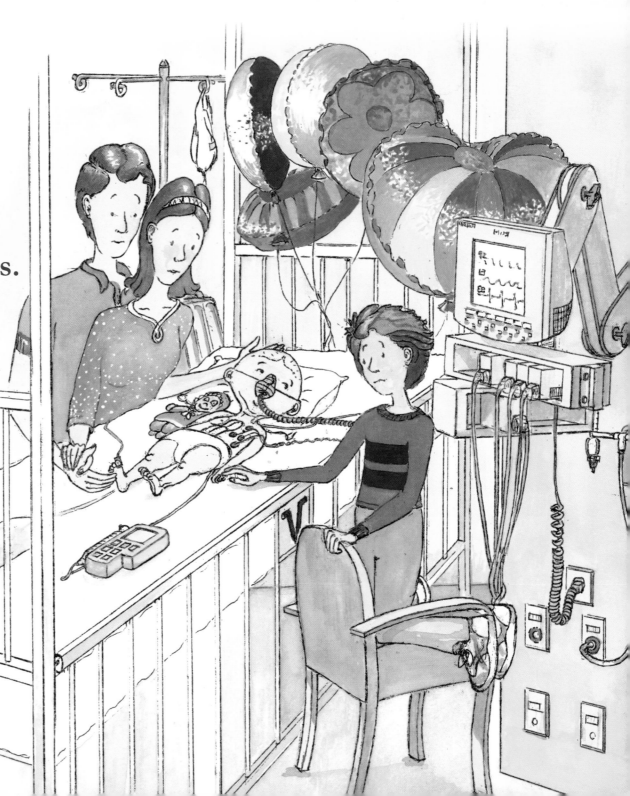

In the ICU, I made a friend named Nathan. Once, we had a sword fight until the nurse said no. I played with Nathan every day until Isabelle went home.

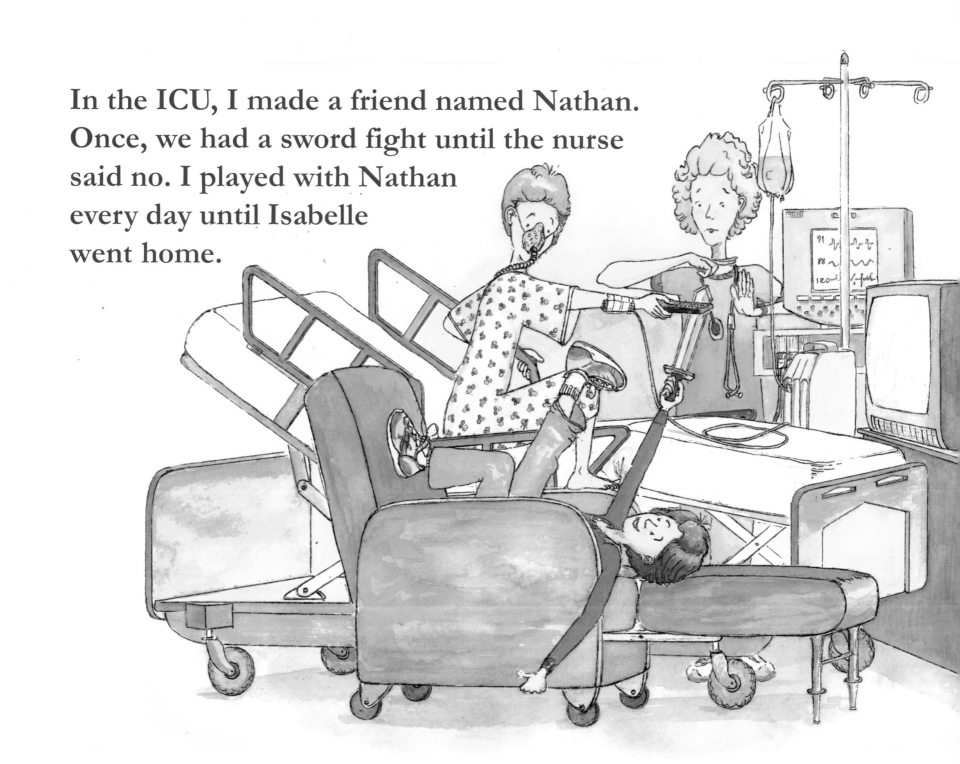

Isabelle got radiation treatments every day until Christmas. That's when they shoot X-rays inside someone's body to kill the cancer. Once, I stayed home from school to see the radiation machine. When it was Isabelle's turn to get radiation, I told her "don't worry little one, there are no ouchies."

After Christmas, Isabelle had a stem cell transplant. That's more chemotherapy, and then baby blood cells to get better. Isabelle was in the hospital for a month. I stayed at home, and helped my mom clean the house so there would be no germs when Isabelle came home.

I remember some good things about the year Isabelle had cancer. People who came to help slept over a lot. Sometimes I miss them. I also liked making Isabelle smile. Mom and Dad gave me a trophy that says I'm the "World's Best Brother!"

This summer, me and my friend Sam sold lemonade at the bike-a-thon to raise money to buy Beanie Babies for kids with cancer. It was the hottest day of the whole summer. We made $229.00.

Every month, me, and my Mom and Dad,
and Isabelle go to the hospital just to visit.
I like to do card tricks for grown ups. They're
always amazed I can do tricks that they can't figure out ...

...but I know kids can do
a lot of amazing things.

I'm glad my Mom and
Dad know it too.

Acknowledgements

I owe my greatest thanks to my son Oliver, who lived this story and approved my words. Isabelle too, deserves thanks for affirming each new illustration with her smile. I thank my loving wife for encouraging me to tell Oliver's story. I am grateful to my family and friends who offered their support and encouragement, and to Oliver's teachers and classmates who gave this book a first audience.

I wish to thank the Jimmy Fund/Dana-Farber Cancer Institute and Boston Children's Hospital staff who offered their critical feedback during the development of this book, noting in particular Susan Parsons MD, Christine Rich RN, MS, Maura O'Connell MSW, LICSW, David DeMaso MD, Stuart Goldman MD, Nadja Reilly PhD, Pamela Hogen PsyD, Aurora SanFeliz EdD, and Summer Holubec MEd. I'm also very grateful to the families of the Dana-Farber Pediatric Patient Family Advisory Council and "Friends for Life" Neuroblastoma Research Fund who offered their critical feedback and support.

I am grateful to Rabbi Harold Kushner for contributing the foreword, and for encouraging me to pursue this book to publication. I offer thanks to Marc Brown for reviewing the text and offering editing suggestions. I am grateful to Elizabeth King for creating and sharing "Kemo-Shark" with readers of this book, to Ce De Candy Inc. for permission to use their trademark "SMARTIES®," and to Ty Inc. for granting permission to use "Beanie Babies®." I am also deeply grateful to Anna Abrams MD, Stephen Chanock MD, Melanie Goldish, Kayla Jernegan, Nancy Keene, Joyce Kulhawik, and U.S. Representative Deborah Pryce, for reviewing this book and offering their endorsement.

I am grateful to Debbie Dean and to Ron and Scott Ferrigno for contributing their professional services to help bring this book to press.

I am grateful to the Davenport Family Foundation and Computer Associates for contributing funds to make this book possible, and to Ruth Hoffman and contributors to the National Office of Candlelighters Childhood Cancer Foundation for having the vision to put this book and others like it, directly into the hands of children across the United States free of charge.

Finally, I wish to acknowledge and honor the many brothers and sisters of kids with cancer who spend a large portion of their young lives loving and helping children during the most difficult of times.

Michael Dodd

About the Author/Illustrator

Michael Dodd PhD is a clinical psychologist and Instructor in Psychology in the Department of Psychiatry at Harvard Medical School. He provides trauma counseling to adults, children and families. Together with his wife, Michael is co-founder of the "Hospital Campers" oncology family support program at Boston Children's Hospital. He and his wife are co-founders of the "Friends for Life" Neuroblastoma Endowed Research Fellowship at Dana-Farber, and are members of the Dana-Farber Pediatric Patient Family Advisory Council.

About Candlelighters

Candlelighters Childhood Cancer Foundation is a 501c3 nonprofit, licensed in the District of Columbia. Candlelighters was formed in 1970 when parents of children who were treated for cancer, felt empowered through sharing with each other about their child's treatments. Community chapters were then formed in each state across the country to provide family support programs. The name of the organization came from an old Chinese proverb, "It is better to light a candle than to curse the darkness." It expressed the goal of the organization to identify the problems associated with childhood cancer and to take steps towards making them better. The National Office informs members of Congress about the special needs of childhood cancer patients, and publishes books and newsletters to teach cancer children and their families about childhood cancer. They have a toll-free phone number to provide helpful treatment related information. Informed families are better able to make decisions regarding their child's treatment and on-going care. Informed children with cancer are better prepared to understand the disease that they are fighting, and informed siblings of children with cancer are better equipped to develop into emotionally healthy adults if they are given the essential information to cope.

About The Book

This book was written to celebrate the ways in which siblings of children with cancer can help during this time of family crisis. Its goal is to promote an increased understanding of childhood cancer, its treatment, and the impact on the family—from the sibling's perspective. This book was written by the author from notes gathered in conversation with his son Oliver during the year that Oliver's sister was in treatment. As much as possible, words spoken by Oliver's character are Oliver's own. Illustrations were sketched in pencil, and painted using ink and watercolors. The interior design and layout was prepared by Ruth Hoffman, Executive Director of the National Office of Candlelighters. The interior layout utilized Pagemaker 7 with text fonts Garamond and Goudy.